£3.55

The BEANO

This Beano Book belongs to

~~WALTER~~ ~~Snooty~~ ~~PLUG~~ ~~Wilfred~~
~~ROGER~~ ~~IVY~~ Smiffy JAMES ~~DENNIS~~

IT'S MINE!

GET OFF OF MY BOOK!

Printed and Published in Great Britain by D. C. THOMSON &
CO., LTD., 185 Fleet Street, London EC4A 2HS.
© D. C. THOMSON & CO., LTD., 1989.
ISBN 0-85116-469-2

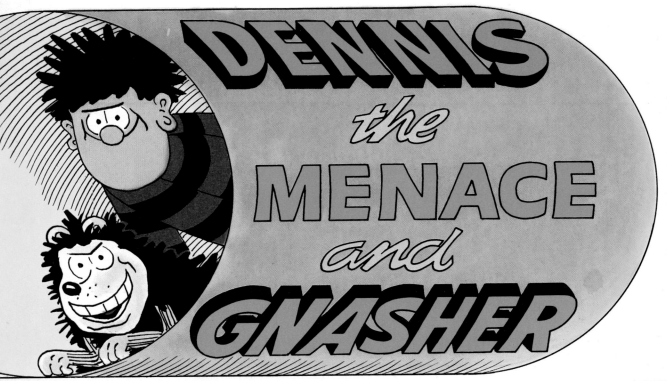

DENNIS the MENACE and GNASHER

BOBSLEIGHING LOOKS BRILLIANT FUN!

GNESH!

Meanwhile at a nearby lino shop —

WONDER WHY THIS STUFF ISN'T SELLING?

LINO SHOP

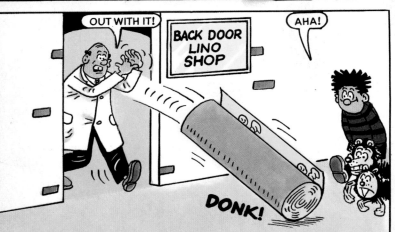

OUT WITH IT!

BACK DOOR LINO SHOP

AHA!

DONK!

DO ME A FAVOUR, GNIPPER.

LIFT!

Minnie the Minx, for a bit of a laugh,
Fires arrows exactly like Cupid.
Is she despatching love and romance?
Of course not — don't be so stupid!

BILLY WHIZZ in
Around the world in 80 minutes

I hired a boat at Bridlington,
And paid out a pound for an hour.
I set off with a splash of oars
Which caused a sudden shower.

ROWING
BOATS
FOR
HIRE

Quite soon some land hove into sight —
I knew it at very first glance.
I'm good at geography you see —
It was the coast of France.

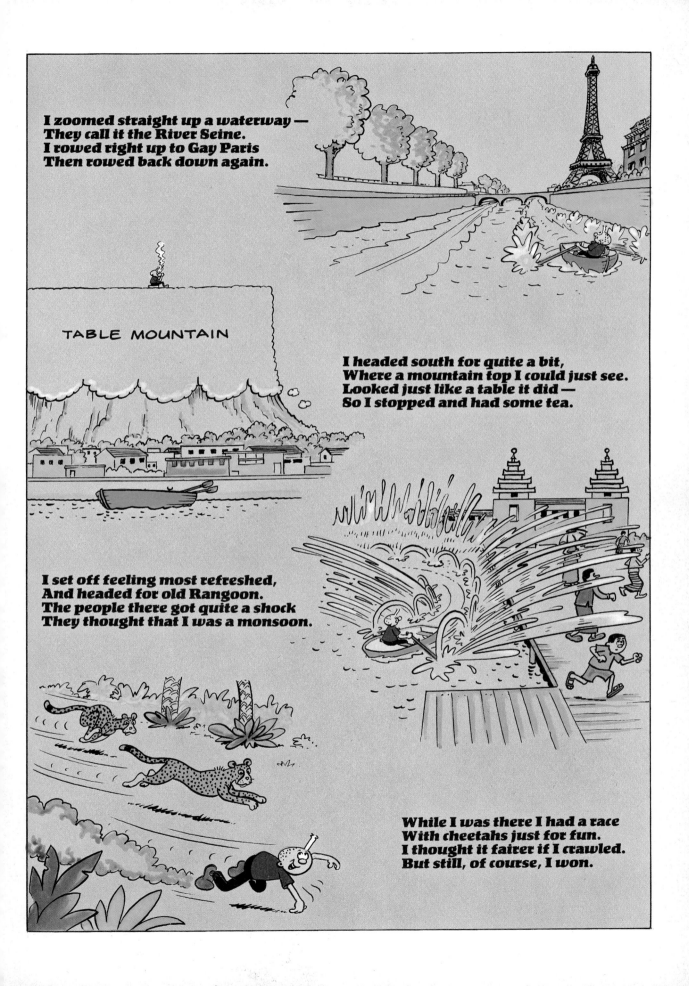

I zoomed straight up a waterway —
They call it the River Seine.
I rowed right up to Gay Paris
Then rowed back down again.

TABLE MOUNTAIN

I headed south for quite a bit,
Where a mountain top I could just see.
Looked just like a table it did —
So I stopped and had some tea.

I set off feeling most refreshed,
And headed for old Rangoon.
The people there got quite a shock
They thought that I was a monsoon.

While I was there I had a race
With cheetahs just for fun.
I thought it fairer if I crawled.
But still, of course, I won.

But very soon I waved goodbye —
'Twas time that I was going.
I rowed so fast I went straight through
An island without knowing.

Just off the Eastern China coast,
Some junks I happened to spy.
I wondered how they got their names
But soon I knew just why.

As I sped past Alaska's shore
I met up with a huge killer whale.
I whizzed straight in his massive mouth
And burst straight out through his tail.

The West Coast of America
Was the next land that I sighted.
The waves caused by my speeding boat
Meant surfers were delighted.

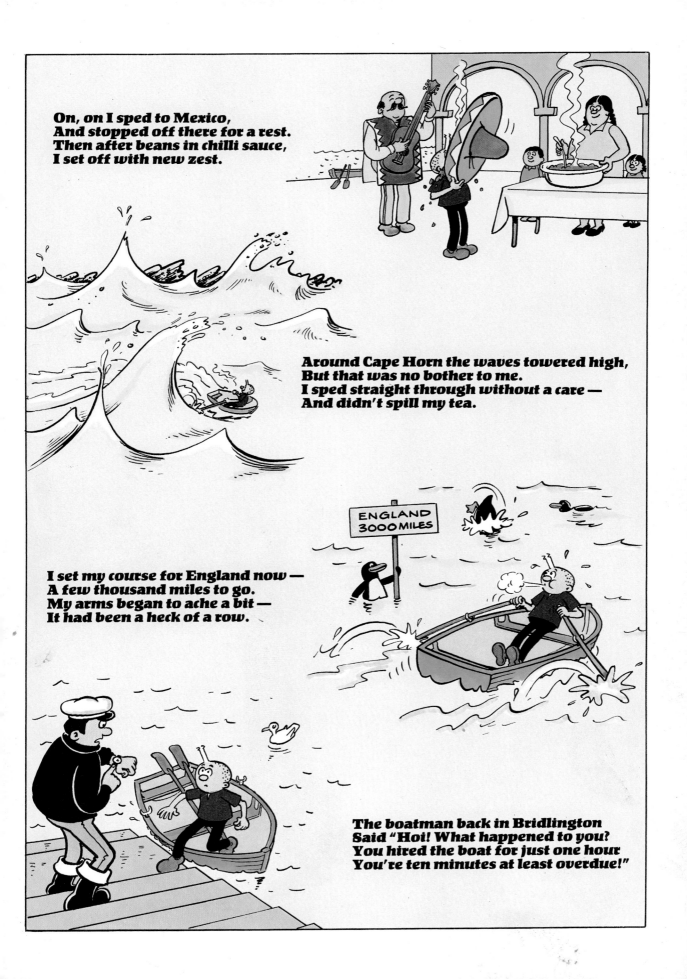

On, on I sped to Mexico,
And stopped off there for a rest.
Then after beans in chilli sauce,
I set off with new zest.

Around Cape Horn the waves towered high,
But that was no bother to me.
I sped straight through without a care —
And didn't spill my tea.

I set my course for England now —
A few thousand miles to go.
My arms began to ache a bit —
It had been a heck of a row.

ENGLAND
3000 MILES

The boatman back in Bridlington
Said "Hoi! What happened to you?
You hired the boat for just one hour
You're ten minutes at least overdue!"

THE BASH STREET KIDS
I ENJOY A QUIET BEDTIME READ TO HELP FORGET ABOUT THE AWFUL KIDS.
TREASURE ISLAND BY R.L. STEVENSON
Teacher's eyes begin to get heavy —
1 TON
1 TON
BASHSPANIOLA
SPLICE THE TIMBERS! SHIVER ME MAINBRACE! YO-HO-HO AND A BOTTLE OF POP.
ZZZZ!
CRISPS
Teacher was here

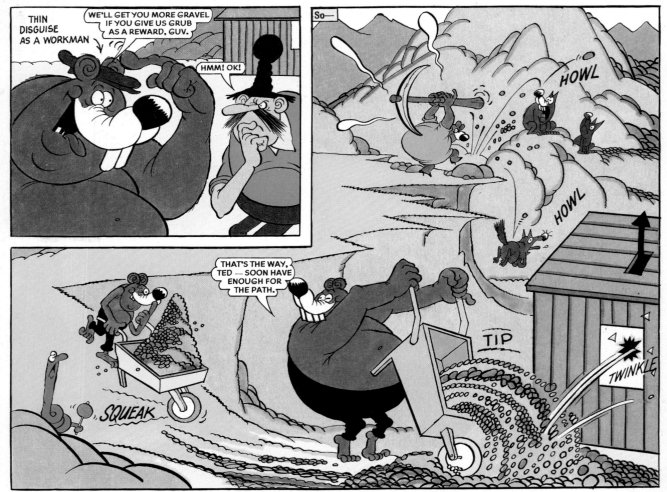

Presently—

THERE — A JOB WELL DONE.

CROAK

THE BILL

COO-EE! GOT OUR GRUB, MISTER HANK?

CROAK! I'M STARVING.

HMM! I'VE SOMETHING FOR YOU IN HERE . . .

SMELL OF MONEY!

CASH

. . . SOME ANCIENT ONION BUNS. ENJOY THEM! HAW-HAW!

RETCH!

WE DID RATHER EXPECT THAT, READERS. BUT TURN THE PAGE TO SEE WHERE WE GOT THE GRAVEL.

TEE-HEE! WAIT TILL HANK SEES WHAT WE'VE DONE.

Minnie, Ivy, Dennis too,
Painted on each shell.
Whoever had this great idea
Was a real EGGHEAD as well!

DANNY'S NANNY

Danny Wilson has the only Nanny in the world with four paws, a wet nose and a tail. You see, Danny's Nanny is a dog!

THAT'S IT, NANNY. GIVE OUR SWEET LITTLE DANNY AN AFTERNOON NAP!

SWEET? WHO'S SHE KIDDING?

DANNY'S HOME-MADE PIMPLE CREAM

OH, DEAR. DANNY'S VERY RESTLESS. MAYBE HE'S HAVING BAD DREAMS!

HUMPH! NO HE ISN'T! HE'S LISTENING TO HIS FAVOURITE HEAVY METAL BAND ON HIS HI-FI!

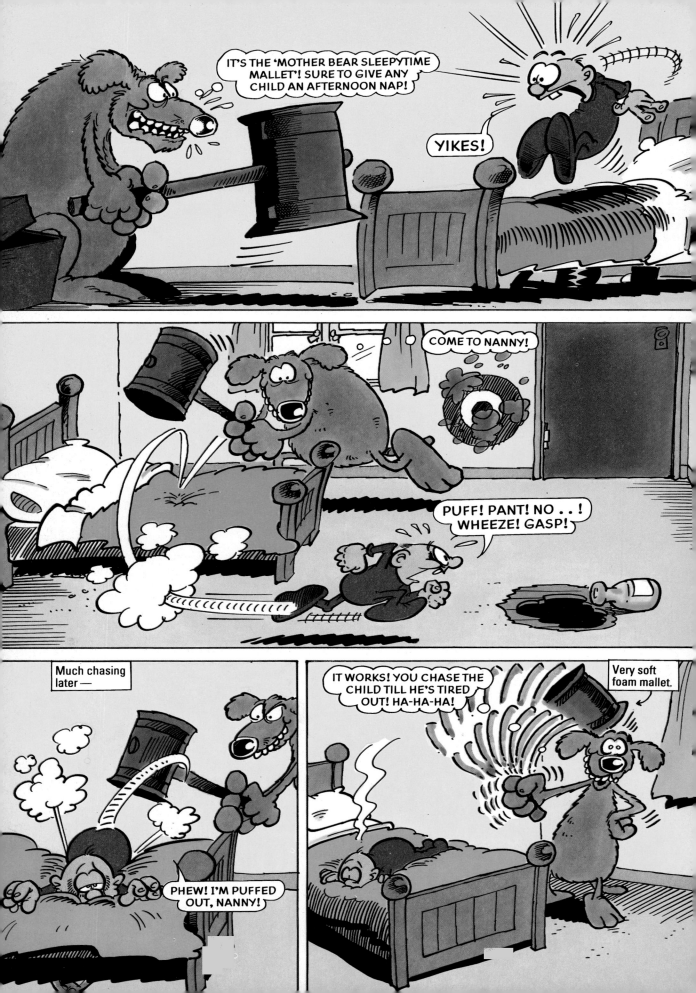

MINNIE the MINX

Soon —

WHERE ARE THE PESTS?

NO TRACE OF THEM AT ALL.

MAY AS WELL READ THIS TO CHEER ME UP!

FOUND THEM!

Inside the comic —

MEET THE BEANO'S NEWEST MINXES, DAD.

WHAT AN ODD PAIR — THEY'RE ALMOST REAL.

GNASHER IN Slumberland

GNZZZ!

'MORNING, CRUNCHER!

'MORNING, GNASHER!

GNASHER

CLIP! CLIP!

COME ON — IT'S TIME FOR THE RACE.

So—

GROWL!

FOO-FOO

HUMAN RACING TRACK

EEK!

AND THE PIES ARE RUNNING

ZOOM

PIE AROMA

SLURP! SLURP!

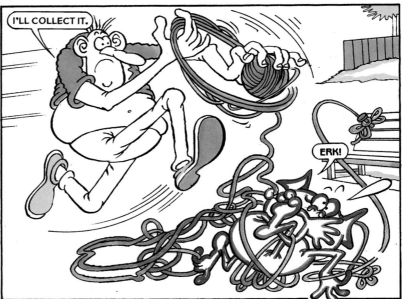

What could be nicer on this Father's Day
Than a pressie from your little boy?
A lovely big bone and a moggy to chew
Is sure to fill this Dad with joy.

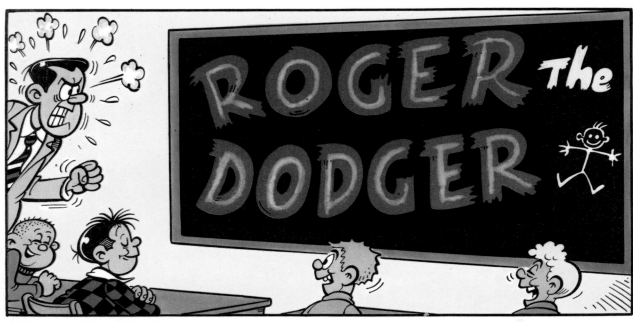

ROGER the DODGER

WHAT'S THIS DOING ON MY BOARD — IT'S TIME FOR A HISTORY LESSON!

RUB!

RUB!

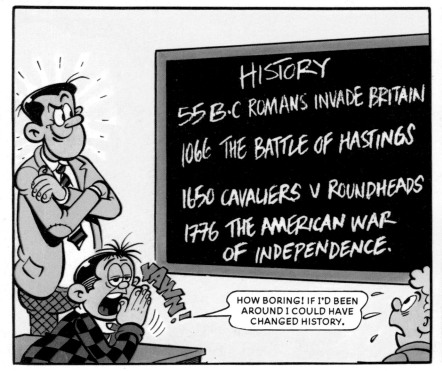

HISTORY
55 B·C ROMANS INVADE BRITAIN
1066 THE BATTLE OF HASTINGS
1650 CAVALIERS V ROUNDHEADS
1776 THE AMERICAN WAR OF INDEPENDENCE.

YAWN!

HOW BORING! IF I'D BEEN AROUND I COULD HAVE CHANGED HISTORY.

HA, YES . . .

SNORE!

ER — FOR MY NEXT TRICK I NEED A GENT'S WATCH.
POP!
BE VERY CAREFUL WITH THAT — OR ELSE!
NO PROBLEMS!
A QUICK SWITCH!
SWIPE!
RUBBER
THAT WATCH HAD BETTER BE OK.
IT WILL — DON'T WORRY!
CRUNCH!
ULP! NOW YOU CAN WORRY!
SNARL!

Be a HEAD HUNTER!

FIND THE NAMES OF THE PAST AND PRESENT 'BEANO' CHARACTERS HIDDEN IN THE WORD-SQUARE BELOW. NAMES CAN BE FOUND IN ANY DIRECTION, LEFT TO RIGHT, RIGHT TO LEFT, TOP TO BOTTOM, BOTTOM TO TOP OR DIAGONALLY. SIMPLY OUTLINE THE NAMES AS YOU FIND THEM.

G	H	M	I	N	N	I	E	T	H	E	M	I	N	X	T	U	B	B	Y
S	C	R	A	P	P	E	R	T	R	E	A	C	L	E	F	O	O	T	R
F	M	M	U	M	Z	Z	I	H	W	Y	L	L	I	B	D	S	O	I	E
B	T	I	D	D	L	E	S	E	G	B	W	L	E	I	O	N	Z	T	H
A	O	R	F	E	T	R	E	B	R	E	A	I	Y	F	E	I	H	C	S
B	H	R	O	F	N	Z	A	A	U	N	L	T	H	F	L	T	N	H	A
Y	E	S	I	N	Y	N	P	S	N	J	T	T	S	O	B	C	E	K	R
F	L	A	A	S	S	U	I	H	T	Y	E	L	I	T	C	H	O	G	S
A	B	Y	N	T	G	N	A	S	H	E	R	E	D	H	R	D	J	R	E
C	I	N	I	O	A	F	A	T	T	Y	X	P	N	E	E	I	E	A	M
E	R	N	G	Y	R	N	E	R	Y	H	L	L	E	B	H	R	L	N	A
F	R	A	N	K	I	E	G	E	S	U	E	U	I	E	C	F	P	N	J
I	E	D	I	M	M	Y	N	E	G	I	K	M	F	A	A	N	M	Y	Y
N	T	I	P	J	S	P	O	T	T	Y	D	X	E	R	E	A	I	L	T
L	E	R	P	K	S	U	R	K	A	E	U	Q	S	N	T	M	P	R	I
A	H	F	E	R	E	V	A	I	T	E	T	T	E	N	A	N	G	U	M
Y	T	L	R	K	N	A	H	D	T	R	E	B	H	T	U	C	V	C	A
S	Y	I	Q	L	O	R	D	S	N	O	O	T	Y	S	P	E	E	P	L
O	V	W	S	T	B	W	F	L	O	R	E	N	C	E	S	U	G	N	A
N	I	D	A	D	R	O	G	E	R	T	H	E	D	O	D	G	E	R	C

ANGUS
BABY FACE FINLAYSON
BEANO
BENJY
BIFFO THE BEAR
BILLY WHIZZ
BONES
BORIS
CALAMITY JAMES
CHIEFY
CURLY
CUTHBERT
DAD
DANNY
DENNIS THE MENACE
DIMMY

ENRY
ERBERT
FATTY
FIENDISH
FLORENCE
FRANKIE
GNANETTE
GNASHER
GNATASHA
GNIPPER
GNORAH
GRANNY
GRUNT
HANK
IVY THE TERRIBLE
JOE

LITTLE PLUM
LIZ
LORD SNOOTY
MANFRID
MINNIE THE MINX
MUM
OINK
PEEPS
PIMPLE
PLUG
PUG
RASHER
ROGER THE DODGER
SCRAPPER
SID
SMIFFY

SNITCH
SNORT
SPOTTY
SQUEAK
TEACHER
TED
THE BASH STREET KIDS
TIDDLES
TITCH
TOOTS
TREACLEFOOT
TUBBY
WALTER
WILFRID

F

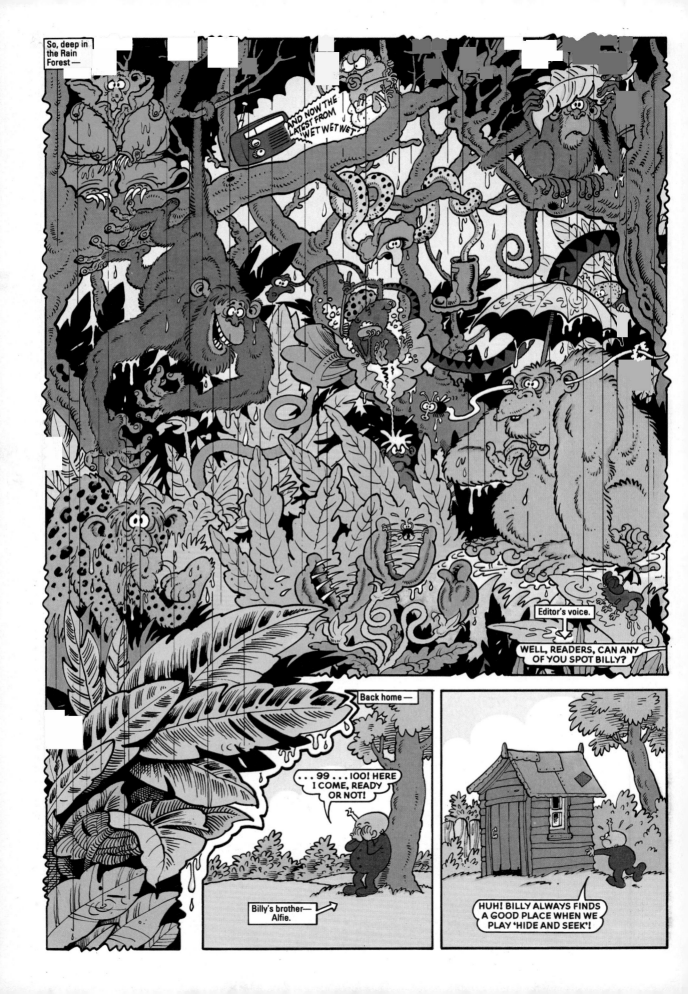

Witches and goblins and spectres and ghosts
And things that go bump in the night —
None of these bother our footballing pal
With his 'ball' with its built-in floodlight.

OO-ER!

NOW I HAVE TO THINK OF A WAY TO GET A BALL AND BOOTS DOWN.

Shortly —

AHA!

THIS WOOL SHOULD DO THE TRICK.

YEEHA! I'M IVY THE COWGIRL.

SWISH!

HOW'S THAT FOR LASSOING?

TUG!

SOON GET IT NOW!

HOI! MY WOOL!

TWANG!

MY JERSEY!

ANYONE KNOW HOW TO GET A BALL, BOOTS AND A JERSEY DOWN FROM A TREE?

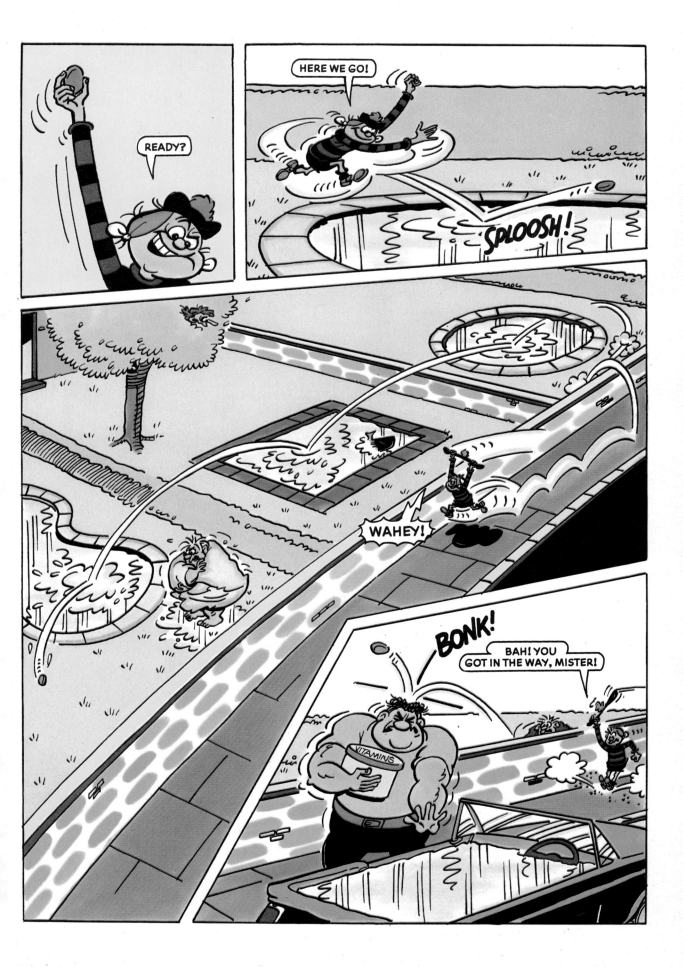

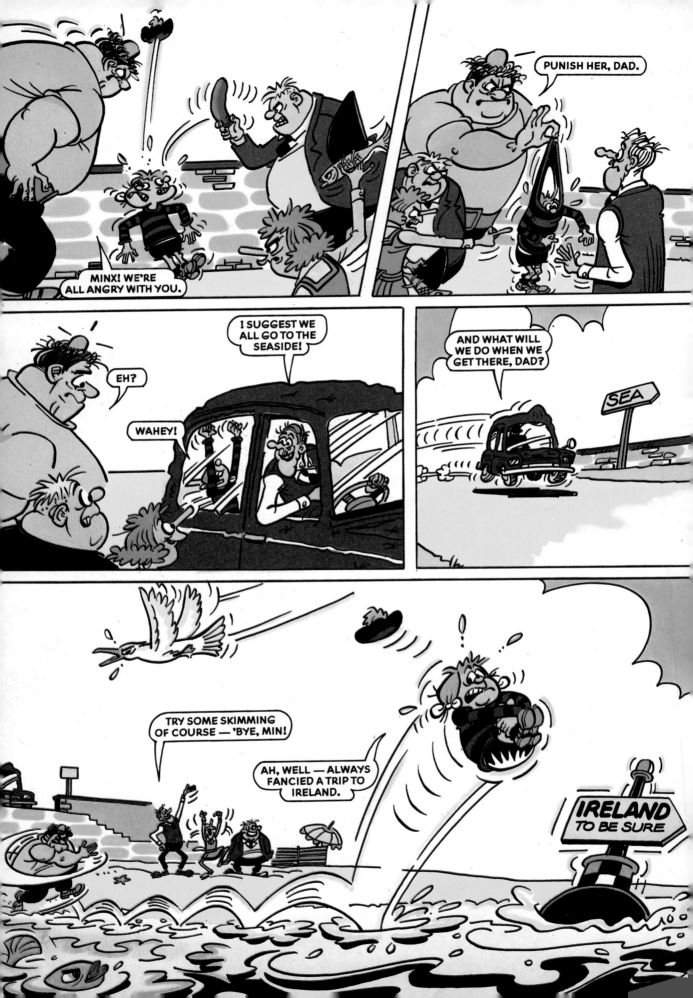

THE BASH STREET KIDS ARE
TO MY SUPER DUPER

TUG!

OF COURSE YOU'RE
ALL INVITED.

HOW ELSE COULD I
SHOW OFF? SNIGGER!

So—

CRINGEWORTHY TOWERS

CRIN
TO

DO COME INTO MY HUMBLE ABODE.

HMM! WHY'S MY RED
CARPET SO LUMPY?

WOBBLE

COS WE'RE UNDER IT—
THAT'S WHY!

HMM! WELL, I SUPPOSE WE CAN STILL PLAY MUSICAL CHAIRS.

WHAT A SHOW OFF!

NO, NO! ONLY "MUSICAL THRONES" IS GOOD ENOUGH FOR ME.

Soon—

WHAT'S BEHIND HERE?

THIS IS AWFUL! WHY DON'T WE GO HOME?

LOVELY MUSIC

HEY, PALS! I'LL TELL YOU WHY WE SHOULDN'T GO HOME . . .

. . . JUST LOOK AT THE PRIZES FOR WINNING "MUSICAL THRONES"!

WOWEE!

WOW! SOMETIMES IT'S NOT SO BAD HAVING A SHOW-OFF IN THE CLASS.

HAPPY DAYS BONFIRE NIGHT

Down the path runs our pal, Den
Being chased by a balding old coot.
If this well dressed guy were to end on the fire
Then poor Dad would be left with a "soot"!

It was a normal day in the life of meter-reader, Alex Tricity, until . . .

DING! DONG!

ODD!

I'VE COME TO READ YOUR ELECTRICITY METER.

WE DON'T HAVE ELECTRICITY.

PROGRAMME

BEANOTOWN
5-A-SIDE LEAGUE

BALL BOY'S TEAM
WEEDS UNITED

**PRICE —
FREE
WITH THE
BEANO BOOK**

**PLAYED AT BALL BOY'S BACK GARDEN.
KICK OFF—WHEN EVERYONE GETS THERE.**

**A SCENE FROM LAST WEEK'S MATCH
WHEN THE REFEREE LOST HIS CONTACT LENS.**

TODAY'S LINE-UP

BALL BOY'S TEAM

Goalie

Black and white striped shirts, black shorts. (Except Dimmy who's wearing a pair of his Mum's bloomers as his shorts are in the wash.)

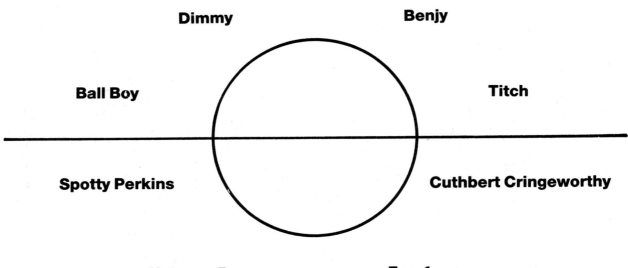

Dimmy

Benjy

Ball Boy

Titch

Spotty Perkins

Cuthbert Cringeworthy

Nervous Rex

Foo-foo

Pretty pink shirts, with lacy shorts.

Walter

WEEDS UNITED

Referee

Ball Boy's Dad if he's home from work on time.

Chairman's Message

None — we don't have a chairman!

Ball Boy's Message

We're delighted to welcome Weeds United today — only because we can thrash then.

WEEDS UNITED

GOALKEEPER —
Walter the Softy.
One of the most agile keepers in the league. Famous for his acrobatic dives to avoid the muddy ball.

SWEEPER —
Nervous Rex.
Made this position his own as he SWEEPS horrid wriggly worms and vicious ants off the pitch before he'll agree to play.

DEFENDER —
Foo-Foo.
Signed to put more bite in the team. Has had a disappointing season since Gnasher knocked his teeth out.

MIDFIELD —
Cuthbert Cringeworthy.
Studious player known for his educated play. Tremendous work rate — does homework while the match is in progress.

STRIKER —
Spotty Perkins.
Just returned to the team after serious injury — he got a speck of dirt under his finger-nail while picking daisies on the pitch.

TRAINER — Bertie "Kiss Your Legs" Blenkinsop.
Employed to kiss it better if one of the team accidentally gets in the way of the ball.

PLAYER PROFILE

THIS WEEK — DIMMY

NAME — Er — Ball Boy — no, Titch, er . . . Pass.

HEIGHT — Pretty Small.

WEIGHT — Skinny.

NUMBER OF INTERNATIONAL APPEARANCES — Five for Brazil, seven for England, two for Albania. (All lies — Ed.)

FAVOURITE OTHER PLAYER — Michael Jackson.

MOST MEMORABLE MATCH — Er — I can't remember.

Ball Boy

HERE IT IS — THE MATCH ITSELF!

THIS'LL BE EASY!

LET'S TOSS FOR ENDS.

OOO! BE CAREFUL, WALTER!

OOER! I COULD'VE BEEN HURT IF THAT COIN HAD HIT ME.

The match starts —

TAKE THAT!

EH?

SOFT SLAP

OFF!

FATTY FUDGE

IN "YOU ONLY EAT RICE"

THE NAME'S FUDGE . . . FATTY FUDGE AND I WANT YOU ALL TO LEARN THE FUDGE THEME — YOU'LL NEED IT LATER!

de-da-da-da da-doo-doo da-da-dedoo-doo

I'M TOLD JAPAN IS THE LAND OF THE RAISIN BUN. SLOBBER!

IT'S DOUBLY OVERWEIGHT AGENT, FATTY FUDGE! WELCOME FATTY-SAN!

JAPAN AIRLINES

NO, THIS IS THE LAND OF THE RISING SUN. WE MOSTLY EAT RICE!

BAH! TRUST ME TO HAVE AN EDITOR WITH A SPEECH IMPEDIMENT!

So—

SUKA SWEET!

I'LL HAVE TO TRY THE LOCAL NOSH, THEN!

GENERAL JUMBO

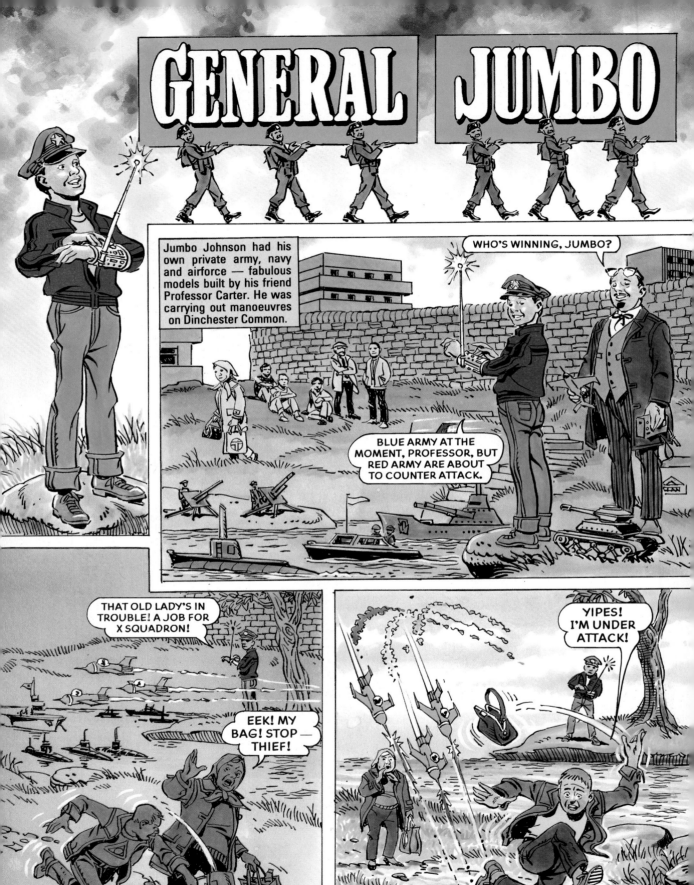

Jumbo Johnson had his own private army, navy and airforce — fabulous models built by his friend Professor Carter. He was carrying out manoeuvres on Dinchester Common.

WHO'S WINNING, JUMBO?

BLUE ARMY AT THE MOMENT, PROFESSOR, BUT RED ARMY ARE ABOUT TO COUNTER ATTACK.

THAT OLD LADY'S IN TROUBLE! A JOB FOR X SQUADRON!

EEK! MY BAG! STOP — THIEF!

YIPES! I'M UNDER ATTACK!

Jumbo returned the bag.

THANK YOU, YOUNG MAN. IT'S GETTING AS YOU'RE AFRAID TO GO OUT IN THIS AREA LATELY, WHAT WITH ALL THE MUGGINGS AND BURGLARIES!

WE COULD DO WITH YOUR ARMY ON OUR NEIGHBOURHOOD WATCH SCHEME. THERE'S A MEETING IN THE SCHOOL HALL TONIGHT.

So, that night Jumbo went along to the meeting.

THAT'S MR JONES, OUR LOCAL COUNCILLOR. HE ORGANISED OUR NEIGHBOURHOOD WATCH SCHEME.

BUT WE'VE BEEN KEEPING WATCH LIKE YOU SUGGESTED, MR JONES, BUT THE MUGGINGS AND ROBBERIES GO ON!

I WOULD LIKE TO PUT MY FORCES AT YOUR DISPOSAL TO BEAT THIS CRIME WAVE, FOLKS.

THIS IS MOST IRREGULAR, BUT WE DO NEED ALL THE HELP WE CAN GET, I SUPPOSE.

After the meeting.

MY HOUSE HAS BEEN BURGLED WHILE I WAS AT THE MEETING!

MINE, TOO!

WE'D BETTER SET UP A CONTROL ROOM.

And that night . . .

SPOTTER PLANES ONE, TWO AND THREE AIRBORNE, PROFESSOR. WITH THEIR INFRA-RED CAMERAS WE SHALL BE ABLE TO SEE THE ENTIRE NEIGHBOURHOOD.

MUGGING IN PROGRESS ON DALE STREET, JUMBO!

I'LL DEPLOY 'Y' TANK SQUADRON!

Jumbo brought in his fuel tankers.

B FOR BERTIE TO JUMBO CONTROL. VILLIANS IN A FLAT SPIN!

THEN BRING ME JUMBO JOHNSON!

The following night.

ALL QUIET TONIGHT, JUMBO.

YES. IT'S A PITY. I WAS REALLY ENJOYING THE BATTLE.

GOT THEM!

NOW I AM IN CONTROL OF YOUR FORCES, BOY! THE CITY SHALL BE AT MY MERCY!

I WOULDN'T DO THAT IF I WERE YOU.

THE S.A.S. AT YOUR SERVICE!

WH-WHAT . . . ?

Night after night Jumbo's forces battled with the villains. Then, at the headquarters of The Master . . .

DON'T GIVE ME EXCUSES! I — THE MASTER — CONTROL ALL CRIME IN THIS CITY! I WILL NOT TOLERATE BUNGLERS!

BUT THE BOY, JUMBO JOHNSON, CONTROLS VAST FORCES, MASTER, AND HE FORESEES EVERY MOVE WE MAKE!

H-HEY!

Jumbo was taken to the Master.

GOOD WORK. NOW I'LL TAKE THIS!

SO YOU'RE THE CRIME BOSS. A BIG MAN WHO'S AFRAID TO SHOW HIS FACE!

YOU FOOLS! CEASE FIRE! I AM YOUR CONTROLLER!

THEY DON'T SEEM TO LIKE TAKING YOUR ORDERS, MASTER!

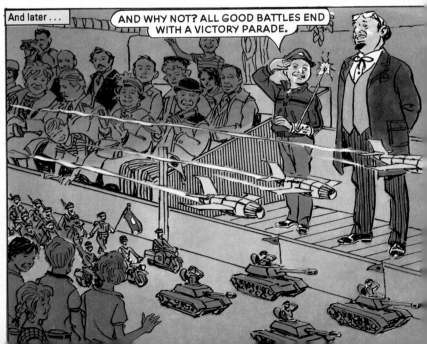

DENNIS the MENACE and GNASHER

SCOTTISH WILD CAT

GNASHER'S SO TOUGH, NOTHING CAN CHALLENGE HIM AROUND HERE.

DAZED

SAS

YAWN!

WAH!

STANLEY LIVINGSTONE- EXPLORER

I'M OFF ON A SAFARI TO AFRICA— ANYONE FANCY COMING?

HEY! MAYBE YOU'D GET SOME TOUGH OPPOSITION THERE!

NUDGE

WE'LL COME!

LEAP

THAT BOY WILL DO ANYTHING TO ESCAPE DOING HOMEWORK.

So, at Beanotown Docks—

ALL ABOARD!

CARRUTHERS

How awful! How dreadful!
How naughty! How shocking!
Just guess who'll find
punishment sums in their stocking.